11 Experiments That Failed

hypothesis

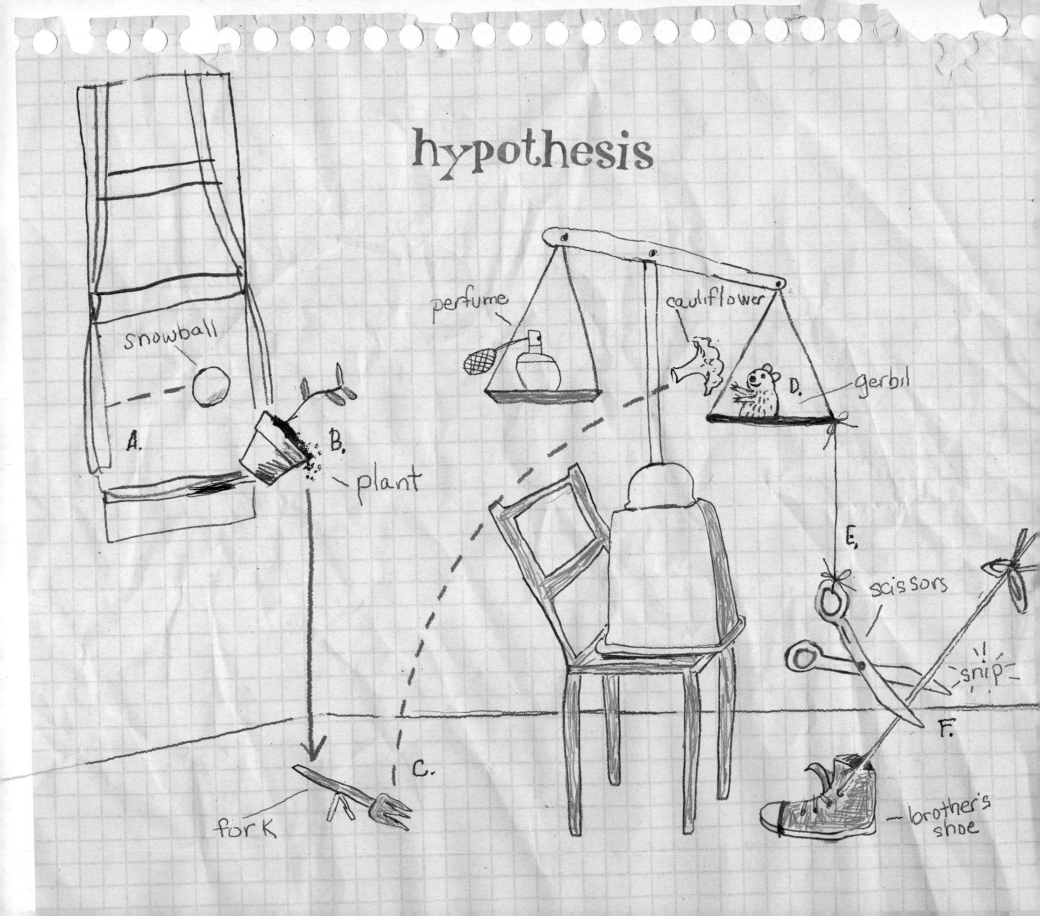

snowball

A.

plant

B.

perfume

cauliflower

gerbil

D.

E.

scissors

snip

F.

brother's shoe

fork

C.

For Theodora
—J.O.

For Anne and Lee
—N.C.

ISBN 978-0-545-57188-3

Text copyright © 2011 by Jenny Offill.
Illustrations copyright © 2011 by Nancy Carpenter.
All rights reserved. Published by Scholastic Inc., 557 Broadway, New York, NY 10012, by arrangement with Random House Children's Books, a division of Random House, Inc. SCHOLASTIC and associated logos are trademarks and/or registered trademarks of Scholastic Inc.

13 14 15 16 17 18/0

08

12 11 10 9 8 7 6 5 4 3 2 1

Printed in the U.S.A.

First Scholastic printing, September 2013

The text of this book is set in Regula.
The illustrations were rendered in pen-and-ink and digital media.
Book design by Rachael Cole

11 Experiments That Failed

written by **JENNY OFFILL** pictures by **NANCY CARPENTER**

SCHOLASTIC INC.

EXPERIMENTS WITH FOOD

Question:

Can a kid make it through the winter eating only snow and ketchup?

Hypothesis:

Ketchup and snow are the only food groups a kid needs.

What You Need:

- Ketchup
- Snow

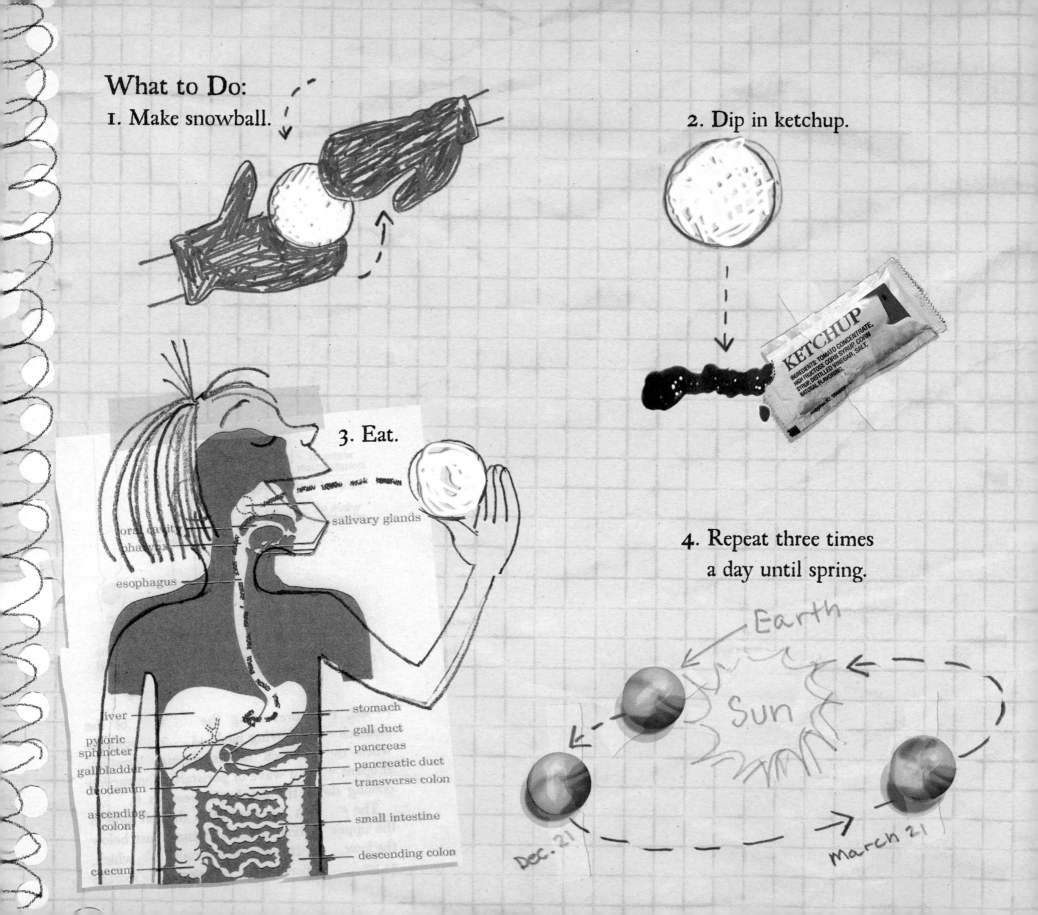

What Happened:
- Stomachache.
- Brain freeze.
- Love of ketchup wavering.

Question:
What makes fungus grow?

Hypothesis:
If left in a closet, food will rot and become a colorful fungus garden.

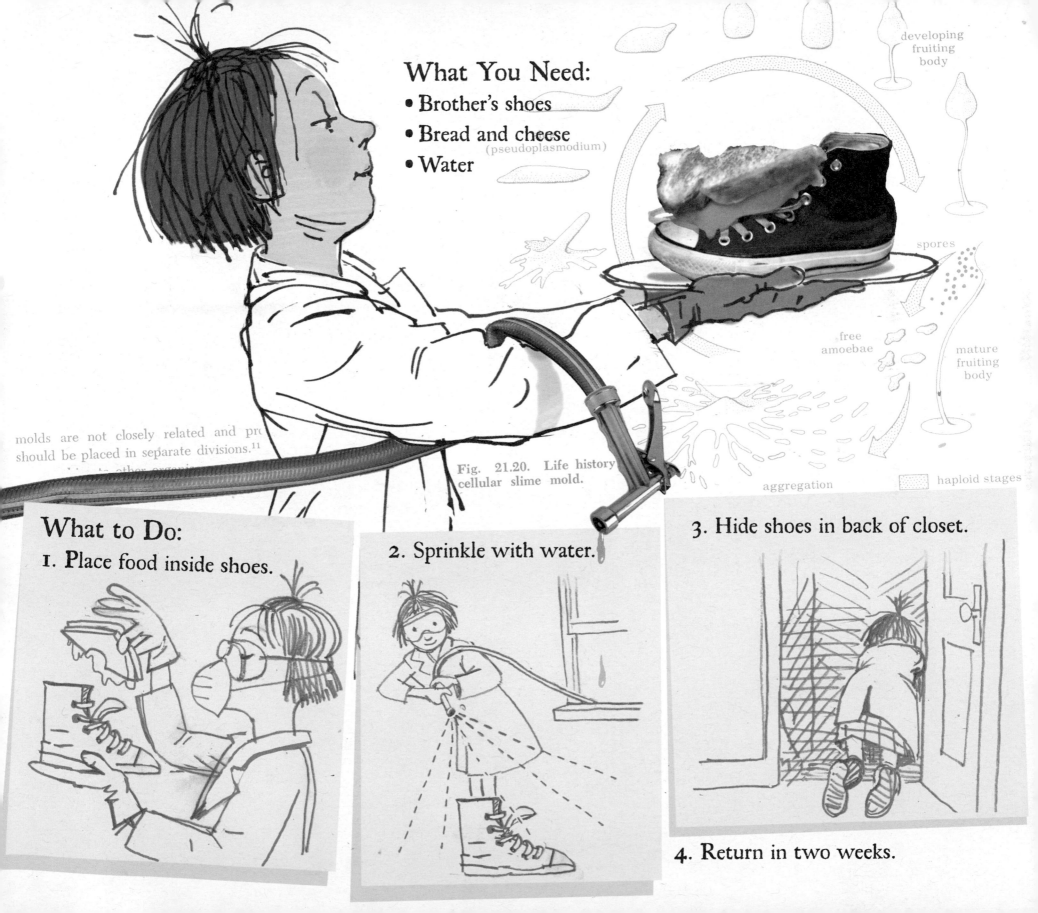

What You Need:
- Brother's shoes
- Bread and cheese
- Water

(pseudoplasmodium)

molds are not closely related and pr[o]
should be placed in separate divisions.[11]

Fig. 21.20. Life history
cellular slime mold.

developing
fruiting
body

spores

free
amoebae

mature
fruiting
body

aggregation   haploid stages

What to Do:
1. Place food inside shoes.

2. Sprinkle with water.

3. Hide shoes in back of closet.

4. Return in two weeks.

What Happened:
Experiment still under way.

EXPERIMENTS
WITH ANIMALS

Question:

Would gerbils like bigger wheels?

Hypothesis:

Gerbils would like bigger wheels.

What You Need:
- Gerbil
- Ferris wheel

What to Do:
1. Take gerbil to amusement park.

2. Strap gerbil into seat with you.

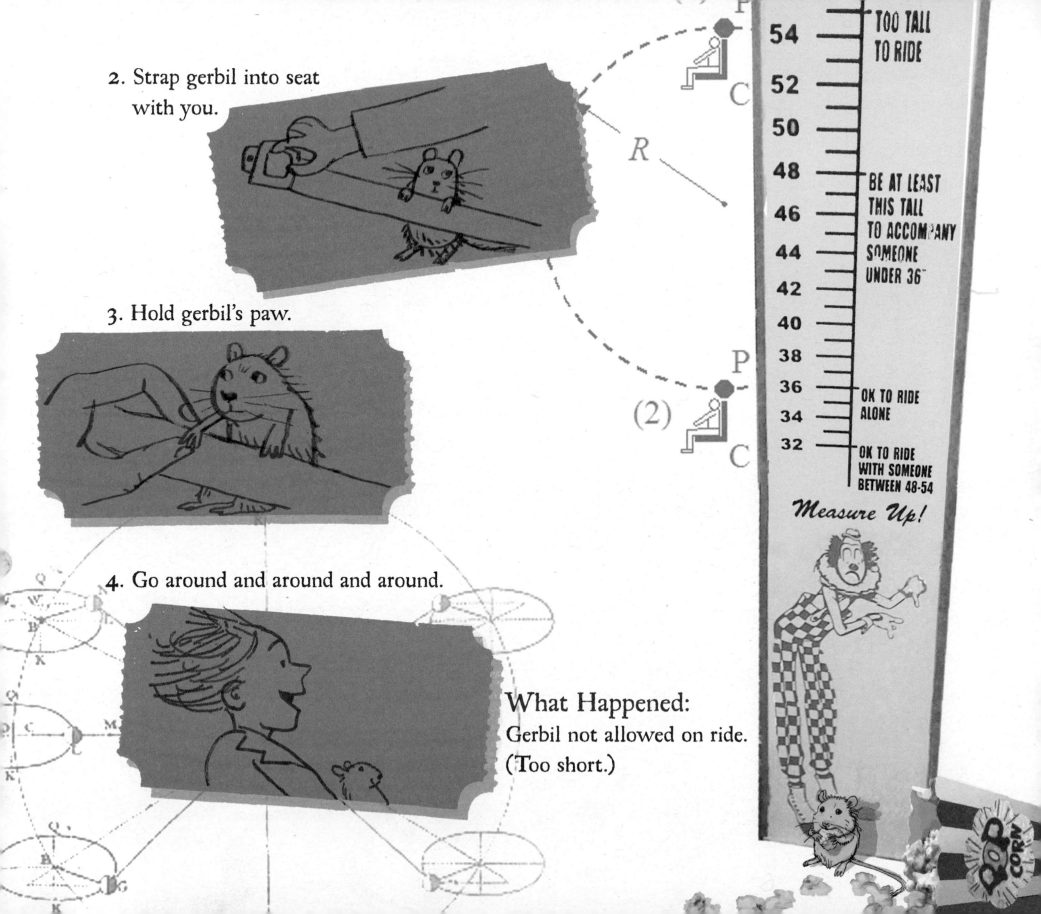

3. Hold gerbil's paw.

4. Go around and around and around.

What Happened:
Gerbil not allowed on ride.
(Too short.)

54 — TOO TALL
TO RIDE
52
50
48 — BE AT LEAST
46 — THIS TALL
TO ACCOMPANY
44 — SOMEONE
UNDER 36"
42
40
38
36 — OK TO RIDE
34 — ALONE
32 — OK TO RIDE
WITH SOMEONE
BETWEEN 48-54

Measure Up!

POP CORN

Question:
Do dogs like to be covered in glitter?

Hypothesis:
Dogs like everything.

What You Need:
- Dog
- Tube of glitter

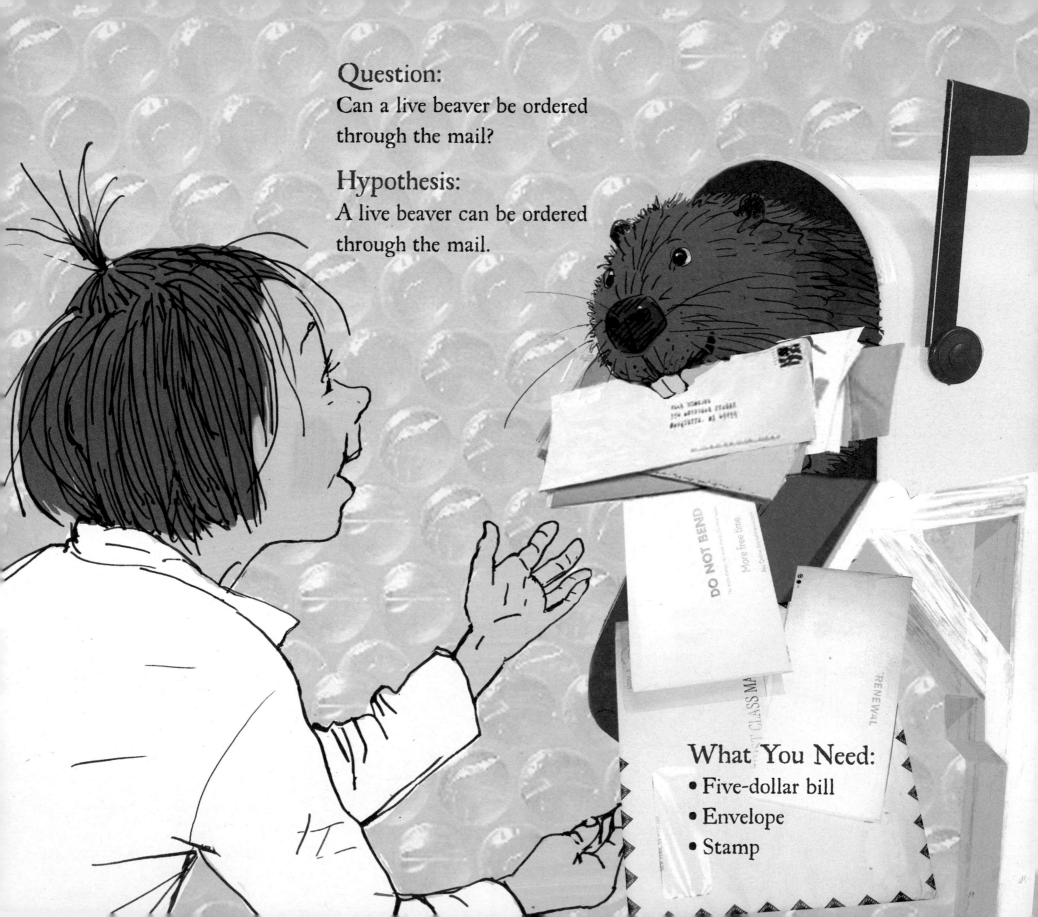

Question:
Can a live beaver be ordered
through the mail?

Hypothesis:
A live beaver can be ordered
through the mail.

What You Need:
• Five-dollar bill
• Envelope
• Stamp

What to Do:

1. Fill out mail-order beaver form.

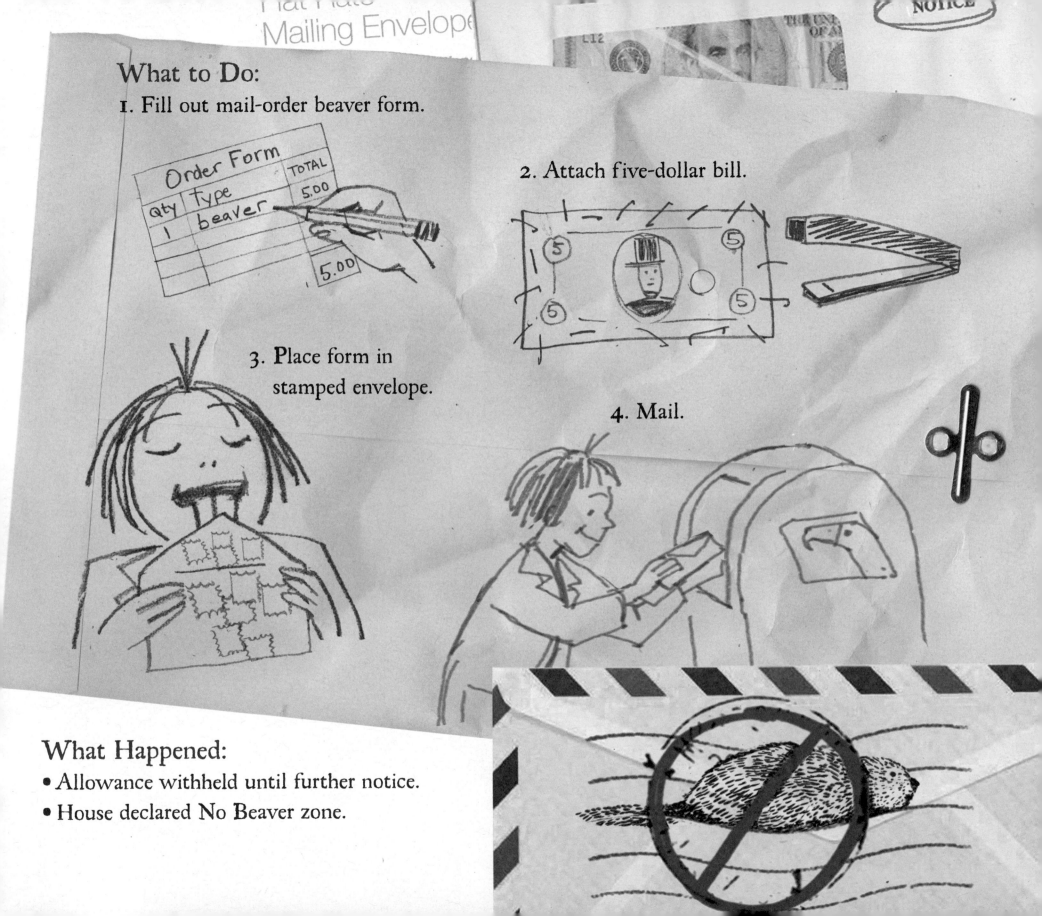

2. Attach five-dollar bill.

3. Place form in stamped envelope.

4. Mail.

What Happened:

- Allowance withheld until further notice.
- House declared No Beaver zone.

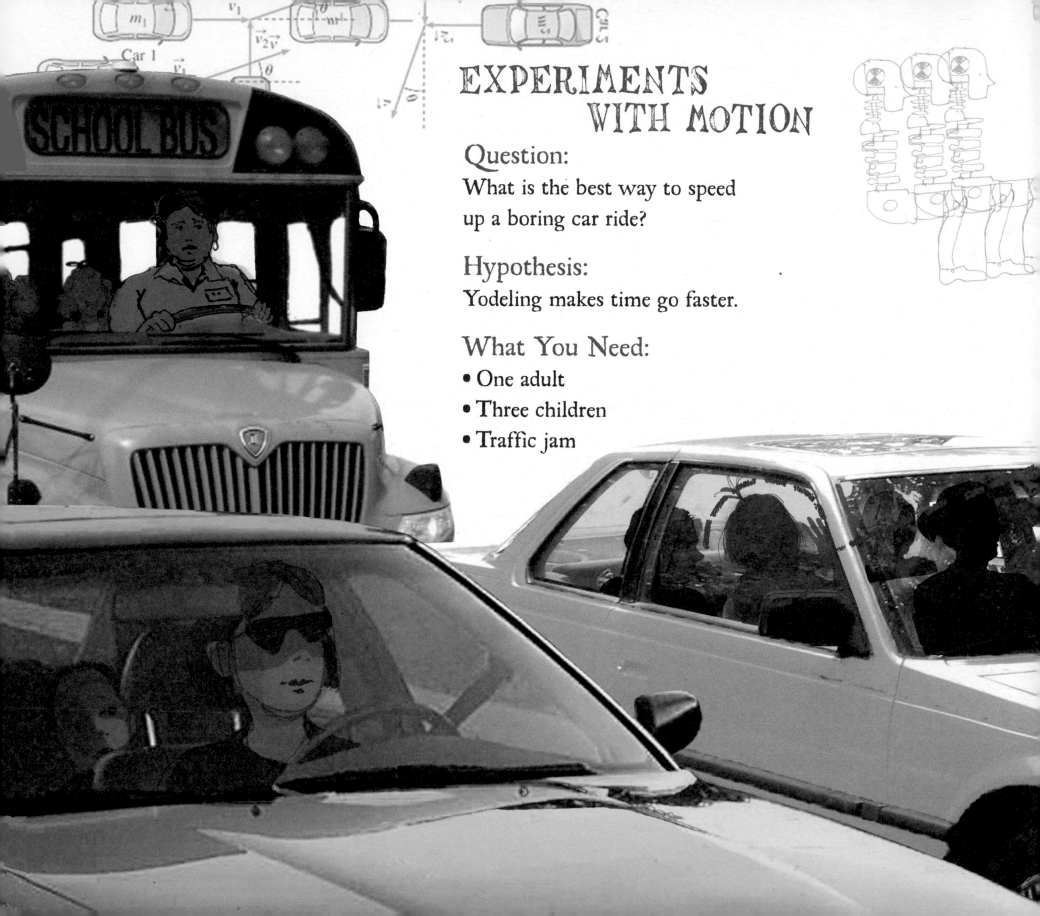

EXPERIMENTS WITH MOTION

Question:
What is the best way to speed up a boring car ride?

Hypothesis:
Yodeling makes time go faster.

What You Need:
- One adult
- Three children
- Traffic jam

30 feet

takeoff point

25 feet

What to Do:

1. Yell "Yodelayheehoo."

2. Yell "Yodelayheehoo" even louder.

3. Repeat as needed.

Velocity (m s⁻¹)

What Happened:
- Walked to school.
- Felt lonesome like a cowboy.

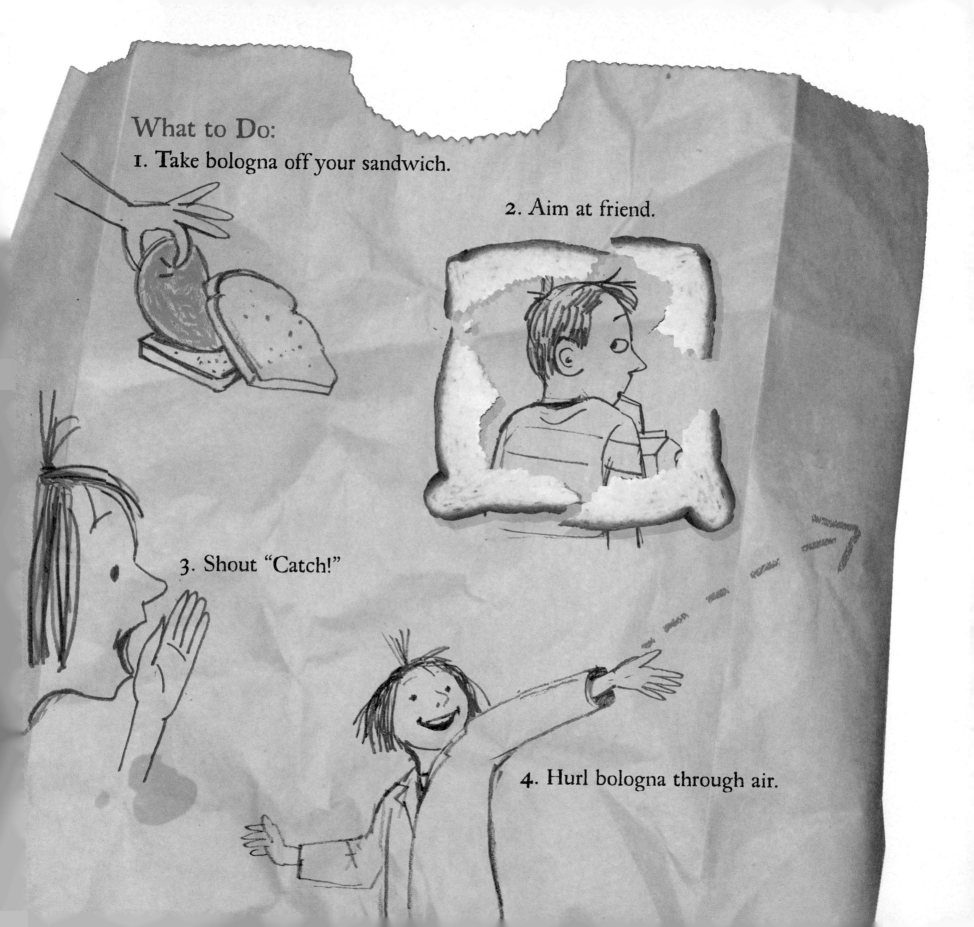

What to Do:

1. Take bologna off your sandwich.

2. Aim at friend.

3. Shout "Catch!"

4. Hurl bologna through air.

Question:
Will a piece of bologna
fly like a Frisbee?

Hypothesis:
A piece of bologna will
fly like a Frisbee.

What You Need:
• Bologna

What Happened:
- Teacher caught bologna with his head.
- No recess.

EXPERIMENTS WITH PERFUME

Question:
Will seedlings grow if given Eau La La instead of water?

Hypothesis:
Seedlings will like Eau La La better than water.

O_2

CO_2

H_2O Eau LaLa

What You Need:
- Pots
- Dirt
- Seedlings
- Water
- Fancy perfume

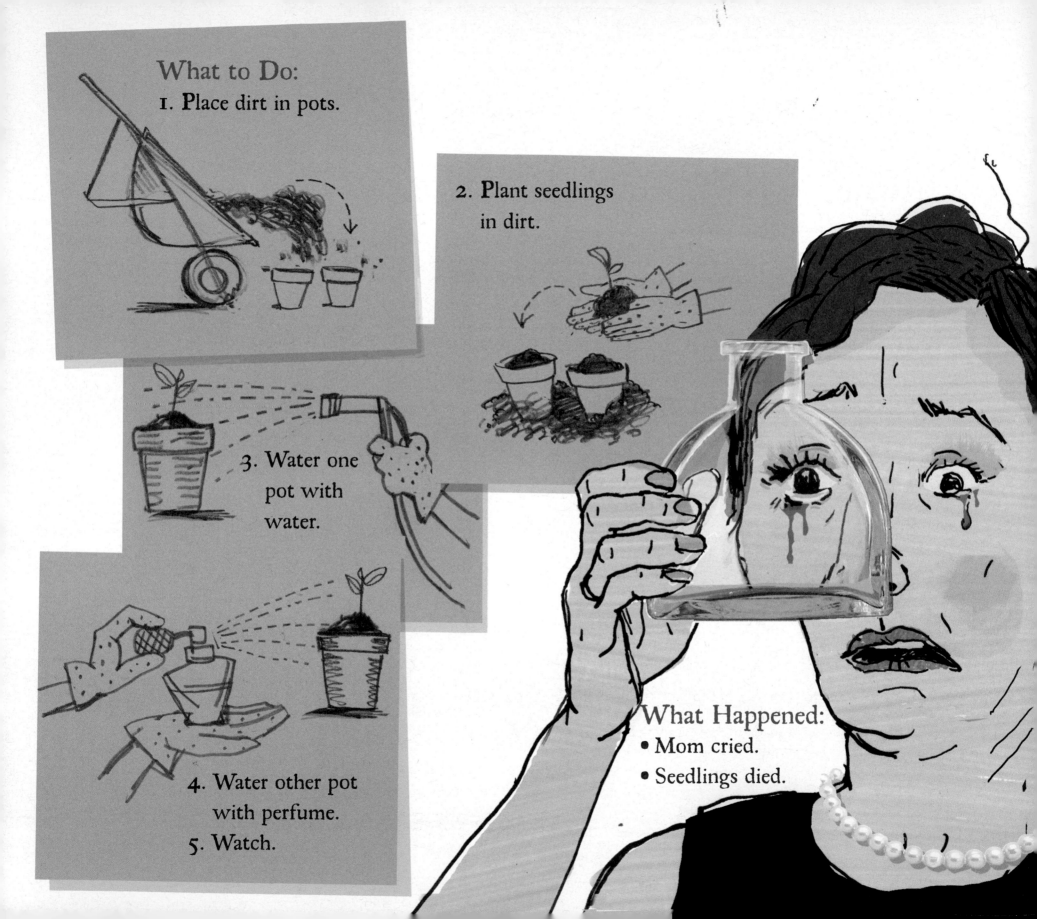

What to Do:

1. Place dirt in pots.

2. Plant seedlings in dirt.

3. Water one pot with water.

4. Water other pot with perfume.

5. Watch.

What Happened:
- Mom cried.
- Seedlings died.

Question:
Is there a way to make stinky cheese smell better?

Hypothesis:
Perfume will make stinky cheese smell better.

What You Need:
- Fancy perfume
- Stinky cheese

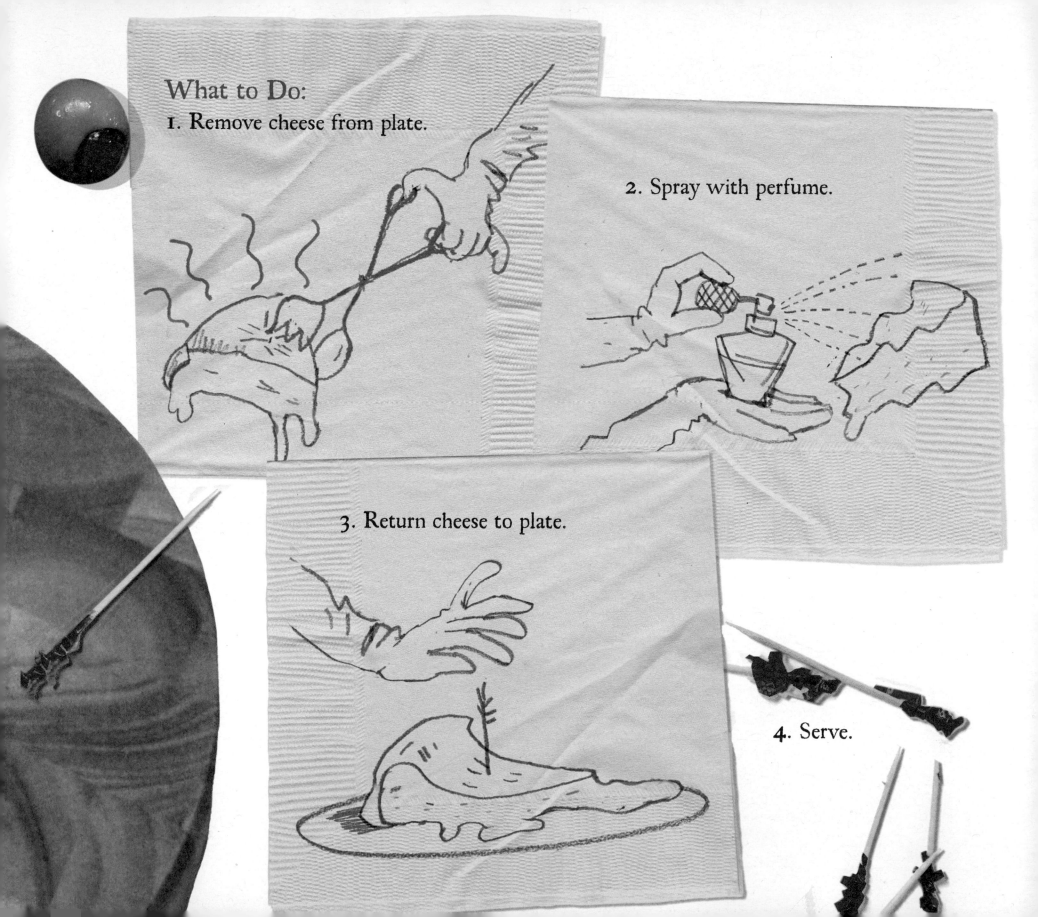

What Happened:
- Unhappy guests.
- Leftovers.

EXPERIMENTS WITH HOUSEHOLD OBJECTS

Question:
Can a washing machine wash dishes?

Hypothesis:
A washing machine can wash anything.

What You Need:
- Washing machine
- Dirty dishes

What to Do:
1. Take clothes out of washing machine.

2. Put in dirty dishes.

3. Add detergent.

4. Turn on washing machine.

What Happened:
- Broken dishes.

- Broken washing machine.

- Ran away to live in bathroom.

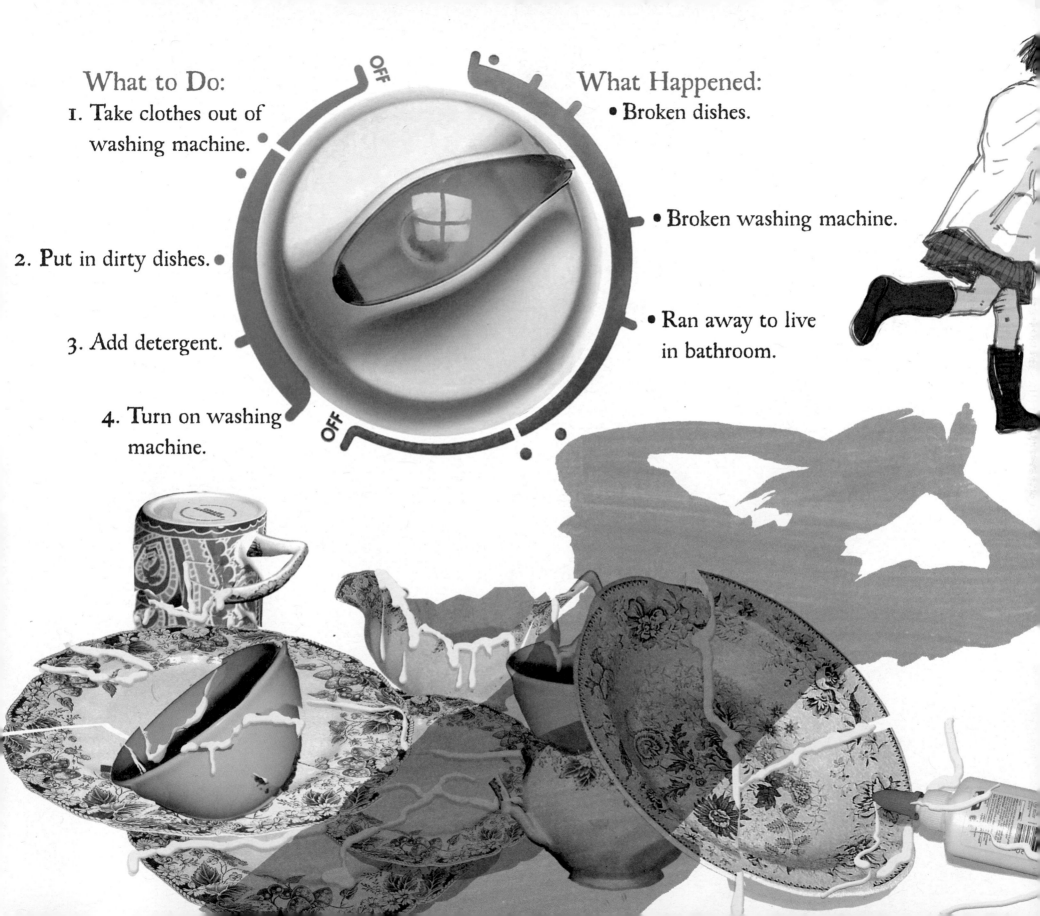

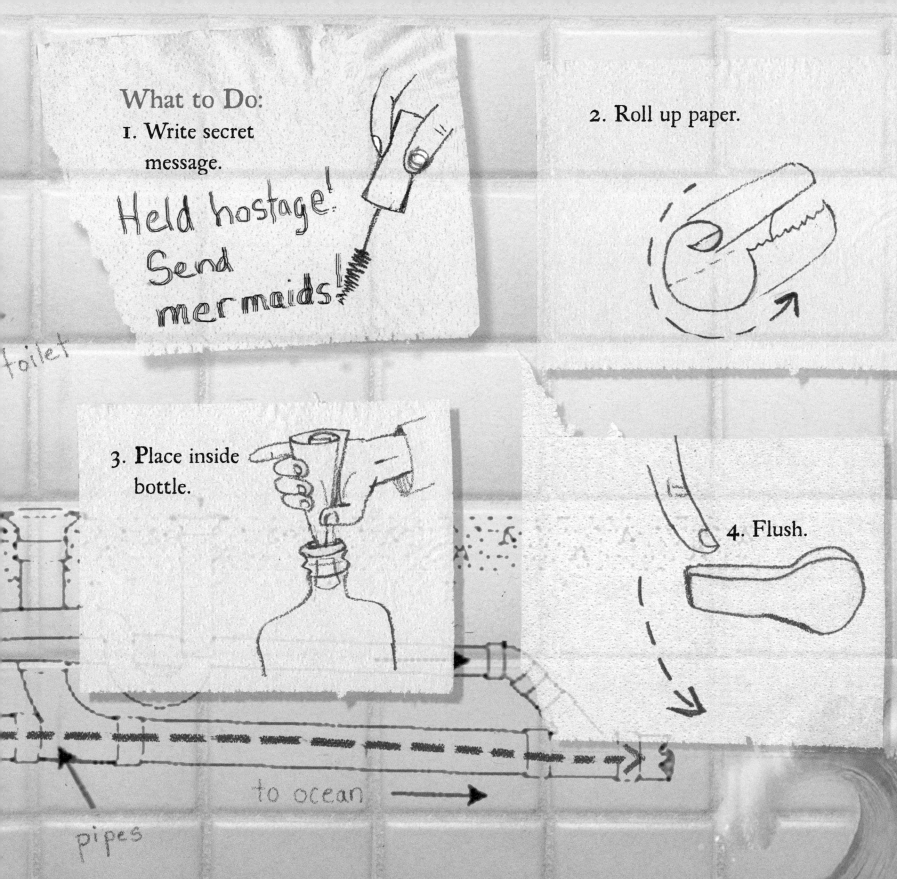

What Happened:
- Toilet overflowed.
- Plumber called.
- Still awaiting rescue.